CHINESE NURSERY RHYMES

CHINESE

Translated by Isaac Taylor Headland

NURSERY

RHYMES

FLEMING H. REVELL COMPANY
WESTWOOD • NEW JERSEY

INTRODUCTION

For many years Isaac Taylor Headland was a professor in Peking University. There he became greatly interested in the children of China—in their games, their humor, and their songs and nursery rhymes, which he found to be uncannily similar to the Mother Goose rhymes of the West. Professor Headland translated many of these rhymes into English, and the Fleming H. Revell Company published them at the turn of the century.

This book preserves some of the most fascinating of these jingles. We present them for your enjoyment, and with sentiments not dissimilar from those expressed by Isaac Taylor Headland years ago: in the hope that they may ". . . lead the children of the West to have some measure of sympathy and affection for the children of the East."

THE PUBLISHERS

CHINESE NURSERY RHYMES

LADY-BUG

Lady-bug, lady-bug,
　　Fly away, do,
Fly to the mountain,
And feed upon dew,
Feed upon dew
　　And sleep on a rug,
And then run away
　　Like a good little bug.

SWEETER THAN SUGAR

My little baby, little boy blue,
Is as sweet as sugar and
　　cinnamon too;
Isn't this precious darling of ours
Sweeter than dates and cinnamon
　　flowers?

9

THE FIRE FLY

Fire-fly,
     fire-fly,
Come from
     the hill,
Your father and mother
     Are waiting here still;
They've brought you some sugar,
     Some candy and meat,
Come quick, or I'll
     give it
To baby to eat.

THE FAT MERCHANT

The
     big
          fat
merchant,
     He opened up a stall,
But had to sell his trousers
     To get the capital.

WHAT THE OLD CROW SAID

An old black crow sat on a tree,
　　And there he sat and said to me:
"Ho, Mr. Wang, there's a sheep on
　　the hill,
Which I wish very much you would
　　catch and kill;
You may eat meat three times a day,
And I'll eat the parts that you throw
　　away."

LITTLE SMALL-FEET

The small-footed girl
With the sweet little smile,
She loves to eat sugar
And sweets all the while.
Her money's all gone
And because she can't buy,
She holds her small feet
While she sits down to cry.

THE CRICKET

On the top of a mountain
A hemp stock was growing,
And up it a cricket was climbing.
    I said to him,
    "Cricket,
    Oh where are you
        going?"
    He answered: "I'm
        going out dining."

A RIDDLE

A plum blossom foot,
    And a pudding face
        sweet,
He's taller when he's
        sitting
Than when standing on his feet.

                    (A toy bear.)

THE BUTTERFLY

Away goes the butterfly,
To catch it I will never try;
The butterfly's about to light,
I would not have it if I might.

OF WHAT USE IS A GIRL

We keep a dog to watch the house,
    A pig is useful, too;
We keep a cat to catch a mouse,
      But what can we do
      With a girl like you?

COME AND PLAY

Little baby, full of glee,
    Won't you come and play
        with me?
Strike the stick and kick the ball,
And at the picnic we'll call.
And you shall come and eat with me,
And you shall come and drink my tea.
    When I invite you
        thus to play,
    How is that you
        run away?

SWEET PILL

My big son,
    My own boy,
Baby is a sweet pill
    That fills my soul with joy.

THE COW

"There's a cow
    on the mountain,"
     The old saying goes,
On her legs are four feet;
     On her feet are eight toes;
Her tail is behind
     On the end of her back,
And her head is in front
     On the end of her neck.

GRANDPA FEEDS BABY

Grandpa holds the baby,
He's sitting on his knee
Eating mutton dumplings
With vinegar and tea.
Then grandpa says to baby,
"When you have had enough,
You'll be a saucy baby
And treat your grandpa rough."

GO TO SLEEP

The tree leaves are murmuring
    hua-la-la,
Baby's very sleepy and wants his
    mama;
Go to sleep, my baby, and then
    go to bed,
And any bogie-boo that comes,
    I'll knock him on the head.

THE TALL MAN

Oh dear! oh dear! just see how
    far
His head is from his feet!
So far indeed he has to bend
    When e'er he wants to eat.
And when he wants to fight a man
    He lifts him up anon,
And when he wants to wash his face
    He pours the water on.

BABY IS SLEEPING

My baby is sleeping,
 My baby's asleep,
  My flower is resting,
   I'll give you a peep;
    How cunning he looks
     As he rests on my arm!
      My flower's most charming
      Of all those that charm.

LITTLE FAT BOY

What a bonnie little fellow is this
    fat boy of mine!
 He makes people die of joy!
What a fine little fellow is this fat boy
        of mine!
     Now who is this loving little boy?

MILKY WAY

When e're the Milky Way you spy
    Diagonal across the sky
The egg-plant you may safely eat,
And all your friends to melons treat.
But when divided toward the west,
You'll heed your trousers and your vest;
When like a horn you see it float,
You'll need your trousers and your coat.

A LULLABY

The heaven is bright,
    The earth is bright,
I have a baby who cries all night;
Let those who pass read what I write,
And they'll sleep all night,
    Till broad daylight.

THE SMALL STORE KEEPER

A wee little boy
    Has opened a store,
In two equal parts
    Are his front door,
A wee little table,
    A wee little chair,
And ebony chop-sticks
    And plates are there.

GO TO BED

Little baby, go to bed,
    We'll put a hoop around your
        head,
And with the oil we get thereby,
Our little bean-cake we will fry.

And when we've fried our bean-cake
    brown,
We'll see the king go into town,
An iron cap upon his head;
Now-you-must-surely-go-to-bed.

THE LAMB

It jumped the chequered wall,
    The bleating little lamb,
And snatched a bunch of grass
    To feed its hungry dam.

OLD CHANG, THE CRAB

Old Mr. Chang, I've oft heard
    it said,
You wear a basket upon your head;
You've two pairs of scissors to cut
    your meat,
And two pairs of
    chopsticks with
    which you eat.

THE MOUSE

He climbed up the candlestick,
    The little mousey brown,
To steal and eat tallow.
    And he couldn't get down.
He called for his grandma,
    But his grandma was in town,
So he doubled up into a wheel
    And rolled himself down.

COMING FROM THE FAIR

Coming from the fair!
    Coming from the fair!
We bought a little bottle
For our baby over there;
    Alas! for we broke it,
    And we tried to buy another,
    But the shops were all closed,
    So we hurried home to mother.

WHAT THE OLD COW SAID

A sad old cow to herself once said,
  While the north wind whistled
   through her shed:
"To head a drum they will take my skin,
And they'll file my bones for a big hair-
  pin,
The scraps of bone they will make into
  dice,
And sell them off at a very low price;
My sinews they'll make into whips, I wot,
And my flesh they'll put in a big soup
  pot."

BEANS

Pull up your black beans,
  Pull up your brown,
Then light up your lamp
  When the sun goes down.

MIXED

Just outside my door, I heard
    someone say,
A man bit a dog in a dangerous way;
Such a message I n'er for a moment
    could stand,
So I took up the door and I opened
    my hand,
I snatched up the dog I should say
    double-quick
And threw him with all of my force
    at a brick;
The brick—I'm afraid you will not
    understand—
I found in a moment had bitten my hand;
I mounted a chair, on a horse I was
    borne,
I blew on a drum and I beat on a horn.

THE LITTLE ORPHAN

Like a little withered flower,
    That is dying in the earth,
I am left alone at seven,
    By her who gave me birth.

With my papa I was happy,
    But I feared he'd take another,
And now my papa's married
    And I have a little brother.

And he eats good food,
    While I eat poor,
And cry for my mother,
    Whom I'll see no more.

THE SLOVENLY BOY

If you wear your
      hat on the side
of your head,
You'll have a lazy wife
      'tis said
If a slouchy coat and slipshod feet,
You'll have a wife who loves to eat.

GRAB THE KNEE

One grab silver,
Two grab gold,
Three, don't laugh
And you'll grow old.

THE LITTLE GIRL'S DREAM

There was a little girl
          and she dreamed,
                    folks say,
That her future mother-in-law
          came one day,
                    And gold and plated
                              presents brought,
                    And a flowered
                              gown and embroidered coat.

THE GREAT WALL

The wily Emperor, Ch'in Shih Huang,
He built a wall both great and strong;
The steps were narrow, but the wall was
          stout;
So it kept the troublesome Tartars out.

THE PAGODA

The dragon
      pagoda,
It touches the
      sky,
The dragon pagoda,
Thirteen stories
      high.

A DILEMMA

Hard worm beans
      Without any bother,
A wife he has married
      And doesn't want his mother.
He must leave his mother,
      Or quarrel with his wife,
And thus they are separated
      All their life.

UNFORTUNATE

He pulled up the wick
    With the candlestick
        knife,
And found he had married
    A bald-headed wife.

Her eyes were askew,
    And her mouth was awry,
And the silly old fellow
    Was so mad he could cry.

CRUEL LITTLE GLUTTON

He ate too much,
    That second brother,
And when he had eaten
    He beat his mother.

A BAD BOY

There was a little fellow,
    Who was mischievous, they
        say,
They sent him to the melon-patch
    To watch it all the day.
They told him he must stay there
    Till the melons all were white,
And not come home to mamma,
    Not even in the night.

THE BRIDE

A newly made kettle is
    bright,
A newly bought pig is a bother,
A newly married wife will not eat,
But cries and thinks of her
    mother.

THE CROWS

Look at the white-breasted
    crows overhead!
My father shot once, and ten crows
    tumbled dead.
When boiled or when fried, they taste
    very good,
But skin them, I tell you, there's no
    better food.

FRIENDS OF THE HOUSE

The thieving old magpie
    has taken our food,
The chicken eats millet as if it
    were good,
The faithful old watch-dog looks
    after the house,
And the cat has come over to
    catch us a mouse.

MY TEACHER AND I

As the sun came up, a ball of
    red,
My teacher rode on his horse ahead,
While I followed close on my dragon
    steed,
       He by
           the street
              and I by
                  the mead.

BUMP

Bump, bump,
    go away,
Do not let our mama see;
If she sees you on baby's head,
She'll give no money for nurse's bread.

THE CAKE SELLER

My pretty little son,
        I love him best of all,
Three years I have not seen him,
        And he's grown so very tall.
My horse he can ride,
        My knife he can take,
Can shoulder up my kneading board
        And help me sell my cake.

THE DEBTOR

The magpie sells his
        bean-curd dear.
If you owe me,
Then you I would see
On just five days from the
        end of the year.

THE UNGRATEFUL SON

The tail of one magpie's as long
    as another,
He married a wife and he gave up his
    mother,
When asked by his mother to buy her
    some cake,
He wanted to know how much money
    'twould take;
When his wife wanted pears he saddled
    his beast,
And started to market to buy her a
    feast;
He took off the peeling with very
    great airs,
And asked her politely to have a few
    pears.

THE MISCHIEVOUS BOY

This michievous boy
Is jumping around,
On his head is a candlestick
    Weighing a pound;
He is able to play
    All the nine kinds of tricks,
From the bell and the foot-ball
    To wood-ball and sticks.

THE RICE SELLER

Someone is knocking loud at
    the door,
The dog is making a great uproar;
Now I inquire, who can it be?
'Tis only a donkey-man I see,
Calling out at the top of his voice:
Here's the place to get your rice,
    Coarse rice or fine,
    Just to your mind,
    Rice in the husk,
    Or cleaned by the wind.

CHICKEN SKIN

I went ten steps outside the
    gate,
Which brought me to the ditches,
And there I found some chicken skin,
    To mend my leather breeches;
If there had been
    no chicken skin,
I could not mend
    my trousers thin.

GRINDING FLOUR

We push the mill,
    The flour we make,
And then for grandma
    A cake we'll bake.

THE FARMER'S GUIDE

In Spring, plant the
turnip,
In summer the beet,
When harvest is over,
We sow the buckwheat.

PULLING THE SAW

We pull the big saw,
We push the big saw,
To saw up the wood,
To build us a house,
In order that baby
May
have
a
good
spouse.

THE DOCTOR'S PRESCRIPTION

A purse, a purse, for better or
    worse,
Indeed would you know it, I've married
    a purse.
My wife's little daughter once fell
    very ill,
And we called for a doctor to give her
    a pill;
He wrote a prescription which now we
    will give her,
In which he has ordered a mosquito's
    liver,
And then in addition the heart of a
    flea,
And half pound of fly wings to make
    her some tea.

LITTLE BOUND FEET

There was a little girl,
    Who would run upon
       the street,
She took rice and changed it
    For good things to eat.

Her mother lost control of her
    Until she bound her feet,
But now she's just as good a girl
    As you will ever meet.

WHAT IS IT?

It has both nose and eyes,
    But it has not breathed
       since birth,
It cannot go to heaven,
    And it will not stay on earth.

(Composed while flying a kite.)

KITE FLYING

There were two little sisters went
    walking one day,
Partly for exercise—partly for play.
The kites they took with them they
    wanted to fly,
Were a big centipede and a big butterfly;
In a very few moments they floated up
    high,
Like a dragon that seemed to be touching
    the sky.

YELLOW DOG

Yellow dog, yellow dog,
    You stay and watch,
While I gather roses
    In the south rose-patch.

GET UP

The day has come,
    I hear the cock;
Get up and dress,
    'Tis six o'clock.

THE CLOTHES VENDER

While out selling clothes,
    As our uncle must do,
He married a wife
    Who is aunt to us two.

She loves to eat cake,
    As you'll readily see,
For she's left but a half one
    For brother and me.

THE BALD OLD WOMAN

On the top of the mount,
    By the road, on a stone—
On a big pile of bricks—
    Sat a bald-headed crone.

On her head were three hairs,
    Which you'll reckon were thin,
In which she was trying
    To wear a jade pin.

She put it in once,
    But once it fell out;
She put it in twice,
    But twice it fell out.

But the old woman said,
    "I know what I'm about,
I'll not pin it in
    And it cannot fall out."

MAMA'S BOY

Do not fear, do not fear,
  We'll put the pants on
    mama's dear,
Do not cry, do not cry,
  We'll put the coat on mama's
    boy.

THE SPIDER

Oh, my dear brother spider,
  With your stomach big
    and red,
From the eaves you are hanging
On a single thread.

THE CAKE SELLER

Round bean cakes with red
    spots bright,
The blind who eat them receive their
    sight;
They cure the deaf and heal the
    lame,
And preserve the teeth of the aged
    dame.
The bald who eat them grow a cue,
And the priest can read his Bible
    through,
They help the Taoist a seat to take.

Their virtues are many—buy my
    cake.
The man who eats fears not his wife,
And the woman works better all her
    life.

THE SMALL PUG DOG

The small pug dog,
    It jumped over there;
It has no tail,
    And it has no hair.

It never will bark,
    If a stranger come,
But runs here and there
    Like a dog that is dumb.

THE MAGICIAN

A big, dead snake is lying
    there,
It has no ears and it has no hair;
    I breathe on it some magic air,
        And it
            lives
                and is
                    running
                        everywhere.

THE LITTLE BOY

The little boy,
    He bought some oil,
But fell and spilled it
    On the soil.

His mother said:
    You careless lad,
I'll box your ears,
    Because
        you're
            bad.

THISTLE-SEED

Thistle-seed, thistle-seed,
    Fly away, fly,
The hair on your body
    Will take you up high;
Let the wind whirl you
    Around and around,
You'll not hurt yourself
    When you fall to the ground.

THE LAZY WOMAN

The lazy woman
    She sweeps the floor,
And leaves the dirt
    Inside the door.

She cooks her rice
    In a dirty pot,
And sleeps at night
    On an old straw cot.

THE TIDY WOMAN

The tidy woman
    Is always clean,
No dirt in her home
    Is ever seen.

Her food is fit
    For a king to eat,
And her hair and clothes
    Are always neat.

THE LITTLE SISTER

My little golden sister
    Rides a golden horse slow,
And we'll use a golden whip
    If the horse doesn't go.

A little gold fish
    In a gold bowl, we see,
And a gold colored bird
    On a gold blossomed tree.

A gold plated god
    In a gold temple stands,
Wih a gold plated baby
    In her gold plated hands.

MY NEPHEW

My nephew is a naughty boy,
    He comes here every day,
He eats until he's very full,
    And then he runs away.

A RIDDLE

A cock's comb flower he wears.
    on his head.
For his clothes he needs neither thimble
    nor thread;
Though you be a great man, I'd have
    you know,
Ten thousand doors would open if he
    should crow.

DON'T BE CRUEL

A mule going up hill,
    A donkey on the street,
Or a horse coming down hill
    You
        never
            ought
                to beat.

RED PEPPER FLOWER

A red pepper flower,
　　Ling, ling, ling,
Mama will listen
　　And baby will sing.

POUNDING RICE

Pound, Pound,
　　Pound the rice,
The pestle goes up
　　and down so nice,
Open the pot,
The fire is hot,
And if you don't eat
I'll
　　　feed
　　　　　you
　　　　　　　rice.

OUR BABY

Mrs. Chang, Mrs. Lee,
Mama has a small baby;
Stands up firm,
Sits up straight,
Won't eat milk,
But lives on cake.

BEAN SPROUTS

Good bean sprouts,
The water dropping out;
Where's the wife that dares to drive
her husband's father out?
He'd take up a stick,
And hit her a lick,
And she could only shake her sleeve
and run off quick.

VISITORS

The wolf has come,
  The tiger has come,
The old priest follows,
Beating a drum.

SHOEMAKER

He stitches the heel,
  And he stitches the sole,
Two measures of millet
   he gets for the whole;
They steam it, or fry it,
  When hungry they feel,
And he eats with his mother
   a very good meal.

TWO WONDERS

All come and see!
All come and see!
A black hen laid a white egg for me!
Oh, look there!
Oh, look there!
A great, big rat all covered with hair!

FLOWER POT

A wee little flower-pot, very deep green,
With just the sweetest flowers that ever
were seen;
Mother with her babies playing very funny,
Father doing business, making lots of
money,
Grandpa very old, but never going to die,
Grandma just as bright as a star in the sky.

THE LITTLE GIRL

The little girl
　　Sits on the stool,
And sews the shoe
　　And beats the sole.

A NEW BABY

A gilt-wood mace,
　　And silvered things,
My grandfather plays,
And grandmother sings;
My grandmother sings till broad daylight,
And a baby comes to our home at night;
They place the child by the pot on the
　　ground,
And it eats rice soup with a sucking sound.

THE FIVE FINGERS

A great big brother,
　　And a little brother, so,
A big bell tower,
　　And a temple and a show,
And little baby wee wee,
　　Always wants to go.

THE FIVE TOES

This little cow eats grass,
This little cow eats hay,
This little cow drinks water,
This little cow runs away,
This little cow does nothing
But just lie down all day;
We'll whip her.

THE FLOWER SELLER

Flowers for sale,
    Flowers for sale,
Come, buy my flowers,
    Before they get stale.

BROTHER WANTS FRUIT

My dear little brother,
    Is fat and is round,
A bracelet he wears on his arm,
    A red chest protector,
    A green pair of pants,
Keep him neither too cool nor too warm.

A small tuft of hair
    On the side of his head,
In his cheeks dainty dimples that suit;
    When he toddles he trembles,
    To sister he says:
"Tum an' buy itty bothy some f'uit."

THE OLD WOMAN

There was an old woman,
    As I have heard tell,
She went to sell pie,
    But her pie would not sell.

She hurried back home,
    But her door-step was high,
And she stumbled and fell
    And a dog ate her pie.

THE DEAD CICADA

The rain has come
    And has overflowed,
The dew and the frost
    Are on the road.
The last of the grass
    Has dropped its head,
The cicada is on it,
    Frozen dead.

FROGGIE

Froggie, old froggie,
    Come over to me;
You'll never go back
    To your home in the sea.

You're an idle old croker
    As ever I saw,
And if not calling papa,
    You're calling mama.

E NE ME NE MI NE MO

One, two, three, and an old cow's
    eye,
When a cow's eye's blind she'll surely
    die;
A piece of skin and a melon, too,
        If you have money
        I'll sell to you;
        But if you're without,
        I'll put you out.

BALD HEAD LEE

There once was a bald-head,
    his name it was Lee,
No one ever burned
    so much incense as he;
Now, people burn incense
    to get them an heir,
But Baldy burned incense
    to get him some hair.

When he found in three days
    all his hair had returned,
He the god gave a coat
    and more incense he burned;
When he found in three days
    all his hair had dropped out,
He upset the god
    and he kicked him about.

Then the god became angry
    and took up a sword,
And made into dippers
    that bald-headed gourd.

WATERING THE FLOWERS

I water the flowers, I water the flowers,
I water them morning and evening hours,
I never wait till the flowers are dry,
I water them e'er the sun is high;
A basin of water, a basin of tea,
I water the flowers, they're op'ning, you see;
A basin of water, another beside,
I water the flowers, they're opening wide.

THE KING WILL WANT YOU

When the leaves are green,
      And full of life,
The king will want you
      For his wife.

When the leaves are yellow
      From time and tide,
The king will want you
      For his bride.

FACE GAME

Knock at the door,
See a face,
Smell an odor,
Hear a voice,
Eat your dinner,
Pull your chin, or
Ke chih, ke chih!

THE BRIDE

The moon shines bright,
The moon shines fair,
The girl wants wedding gifts to wear
in her hair;
A few blocks of powder,
Some incense tips,
And two hundred rouge-pads to paint
cheeks and lips.

DO AS YOU OUGHT

In the first month,
    when it is night,
If you are wise,
    your lamp you'll light;
And when the second
    month you meet,
If you are hungry
    you should eat;
And in the third month
    most of all,
To build a house
    you must lay a wall.

FINGER TEST

You strike three times on the top, you see,
And strike three times on the bottom for me,
Then top and bottom you strike very fast,
And open a door in the middle at last.

TEN FINGERS

Three horses are drinking,
    Three horses are feeding,
The two men are fighting,
    The old woman pleading,
The baby is crying,
    But no one is heeding.

DON'T STEAL

If you steal a needle,
    Or steal a thread,
A pimple will grow
    Upon your head;
If you steal a dog
    Or steal a cat,
A pimple will grow
    Beneath your hat.